Pokémon

GHOST, DARK, & STEEL
HANDBOOK

By Tracey West
and Katherine Noll

D1287353

SCHOLASTIC INC.
New York Toronto London Auckland Sydney
Mexico City New Delhi Hong Kong Buenos Aires

ISBN 0-439-80174-5

Published by Scholastic Inc.
SCHOLASTIC and associated logos are trademarks and/or
registered trademarks of Scholastic Inc.

12 11 10 9 8 7 6 5 4 3 2   5 6 7 8 9/0

Interior designed by Two Red Shoes Design

Printed in the U.S.A.
First printing, November 2005

THREE TERRIFYING TYPES

Do you think **Igglybuff** is a tough Pokémon? Do you dream of training a team of **Wooper**? If so, then this Pokémon handbook is NOT for you!

Sure, there's nothing wrong with cute Pokémon. Most Trainers have a soft spot for them. But if you really want to take control of the battlefield, you need some tough Pokémon on your team. That's where this special handbook comes in: It has everything you need to know about spooky Ghost-types, scary Dark-types, and supersolid Steel-types. Once you master these three types, other Trainers will fear your skills. And that's a good thing.

So if you're brave enough, keep reading. This handbook will give you:

- **Complete stats for 38 Pokémon.**
- **Tips for using Ghost, Dark, and Steel-type Pokémon in battle.**
- **The best places to find these Pokémon types.**
- **Stories of some epic Pokémon battles.**
- **And facts that every Pokémon Trainer should know!**

While you're exploring this handbook, you'll come across some special Pokémon terms. Here is a list to help you on your journey:

MOVES: Each Pokémon has special attacks that it uses in battle. Different Pokémon know different moves.

EVOLUTION: When a Pokémon evolves, it changes into a new form. **Gastly** evolves into **Haunter**. **Aron** evolves into **Lairon**. This book will tell you when or if that happens to a Pokémon.

TYPE: Each Pokémon is identified with a type. Some types are Fire, Water, or Grass. The type of Pokémon you have determines what kinds of Pokémon yours will be effective against in battle. A Pokémon can also be more than one type. **Murkrow** is a Dark-and-Flying-type Pokémon.

Are you ready yet? Good! It's time to explore the mysterious world of Ghost, Dark, and Steel-type Pokémon!

Hi! Professor Birch here. I live in Littleroot Town in the Hoenn Region. I help new Pokémon Trainers begin their journeys.

If you are reading this handbook, you must be a very dedicated Trainer. Only the most serious Trainers would decide to take on training Ghost, Dark, or Steel-type Pokémon. They are powerful types, but they can be difficult to train. Here's what you can expect if you choose to add these Pokémon to your team.

GHOST-TYPES

If you go searching for Ghost-type Pokémon, don't expect to find them waiting for you to catch them. They like to hide in the shadows, and pop up when you least expect them. Their moves can take you by surprise. Take Confuse Ray, for example. In this move, a Pokémon sends out a powerful beam. When the beam hits the opponent, it can cause the opponent to become confused. The opponent often hurts itself when it becomes confused. If you are afraid of the dark, you might want to think twice before training Ghost-type Pokémon. Most of them can be found in dark and spooky places, such as run-down houses and abandoned towers. This handbook will tell you the very best places to find Ghost-type Pokémon—if you dare.

STEEL-TYPE POKÉMON •

DARK-TYPES

Dark-type Pokémon may not mean to frighten you, but they can definitely be scary! Dark-type Pokémon are also fond of playing dangerous tricks on people. And with such sneaky moves as Snatch, Taunt, Torment, and Thief, it's easy to be tricked in battle as well.

Dark-type Pokémon share some of the same moves as Ghost-type Pokémon. One move both types use is Screech. That's when a Pokémon makes a loud, high-pitched noise. The noise is so terrible that it lowers the Defense of the opponent!

STEEL-TYPES

Steel-type Pokémon might not be spooky or mean, but they're just as dangerous. Most of them have sharp wings, claws, or fangs. That's because their bodies—or parts of their bodies—are made out of solid steel.

But Steel-type Pokémon are most famous for their defensive abilities. They don't get tired as quickly as other Pokémon, and they have powerful bodies that can take a lot of damage. In fact, some of them are practically unstoppable!

There is a lot more to learn about Ghost, Dark, and Steel-type Pokémon if you want to master them. So what are you waiting for? It's time to check out these three tough types.

· BATTLE TIPS FOR GHOST-TYPE POKÉMON ·

One of the things a Pokémon Trainer needs to know is which Pokémon to choose in a battle. If you battle with a Ghost Pokémon, this chart will help you know which moves will do the most—or the least—damage to other Pokémon.

GHOST-TYPES ARE GOOD AGAINST:

Other Ghost-type Pokémon. If your opponent whips out a **Misdreavus**, why not call on your **Gastly** and see what happens? It's sure to be an interesting battle.

GHOST-TYPES ARE BAD AGAINST:

- **Dark-types such as Umbreon.**
- **Steel-types such as Mawile.**
- **Normal-types such as Meowth.**

Now you know how to battle with your Ghost-type Pokémon. But that's not all you need to know to train these chilling types. Keep reading to get the stats on every known Ghost-type in the world of Pokémon!

Aiiiiieeeeeee! What's that spooky scream? It might be **Misdreavus**. This Pokémon loves to scare people by suddenly screaming or wailing—especially in the middle of the night! Other times, it lets out a spooky sob that is sure to give you the chills.

Misdreavus has another trick. It likes to sneak up on people and bite or pull their hair! That might not seem very nice. But **Misdreavus** has a reason to scare people. It can turn fear into food that it can eat! Isn't that amazing? You'd be a lucky Trainer if you could find and catch **Misdreavus**.

MISDREAVUS

Screech Pokémon

How to Say It: miss-DREE-vuss
Possible Moves: Growl, Psywave, Spite, Astonish, Confuse Ray, Mean Look, Psybeam, Pain Split, Perish Song, Grudge
Does not evolve
Type: Ghost
Height: 2' 4"
Weight: 2 lbs

Bring a Silph Scope if you travel to the Pokémon Tower in Kanto's Lavender Town. The Silph Scope allows you to see invisible Ghost-type Pokémon. Once you spot them, you can try to catch them!

7

KANTO

Gastly and Haunter are the two lightest Pokémon around. But they have some pretty heavy-duty moves! Gastly is made out of gas. It can sneak into any place it wants, and then scare you. Haunter can float right through walls! This Pokémon's tongue is made out of poison gas. If it licks you, watch out!

If you feel a sudden chill next to you, you might be near Haunter's evolved form, Gengar. Creepy Gengar likes to hide in the shadows. You need to be a brave Trainer to work with these three terrors!

GASTLY

Gas Pokémon

How to Say It: GAST-lee
Possible Moves: Lick, Spite, Curse, Confuse Ray, Night Shade, Hypnosis, Dream Eater, Destiny Bond, Shadow Ball, Mean Look, Nightmare
Evolves: at level 25
Dual Type: Ghost-Poison
Height: 4' 3"
Weight: 0.2 lbs

HAUNTER

Gas Pokémon

How to Say It: HAWN-ter

Possible Moves: Lick, Spite, Confuse Ray, Night Shade, Hypnosis, Dream Eater, Destiny Bond, Shadow Ball, Nightmare, Mean Look, Shadow Punch

Evolves: with a Trade

Dual Type: Ghost-Poison

Height: 5' 3"

Weight: 0.2 lbs

GENGAR

Shadow Pokémon

How to Say It: GANG-are

Possible Moves: Lick, Spite, Confuse Ray, Night Shade, Hypnosis, Dream Eater, Destiny Bond, Shadow Ball, Nightmare, Mean Look, Shadow Punch

Does not evolve

Dual Type: Ghost-Poison

Height: 4' 11"

Weight: 89 lbs

HOENN

Something weird happens when **Shedinja** evolves from the Bug-and-Ground-type Pokémon **Nincada**. **Shedinja** becomes a Bug-and-Ghost-type Pokémon with a hard shell. But people believe there is nothing inside the shell. It's hollow!

If you want a **Shedinja**, don't go looking for one. A **Shedinja** will mysteriously appear inside an empty Poké Ball. But don't get too excited. **Shedinja** does not move at all. It doesn't even breathe! Nobody is really sure how it performs its attacks.

Nincada
(Bug-Ground type)

SHEDINJA

Shed Pokémon

How to Say It: shed-IN-juh
Possible Moves: Scratch, Harden, Leech Life, Sand-Attack, Fury Swipes, Mind Reader, Spite, Confuse Ray, Shadow Ball, Grudge
Does not evolve
Dual Type: Bug-Ghost
Height: 2' 7"
Weight: 3 lbs

Tip

Spell Tag is a great item for your Ghost-type Pokémon to have. It will increase the power of its attacks!

HOENN

One of these Pokémon looks like a puppet. The other looks like a stuffed toy. But do not play around with them, whatever you do! **Shuppet** and **Banette** can be dangerous.

Shuppet floats around, looking for people who are jealous. It feeds on bad feelings. **Banette** likes to place curses on its opponents. Yikes! Better put these Pokémon back in the toy box!

SHUPPET

Puppet Pokémon
How to Say It: SHUH-pet
Possible Moves: Knock Off, Screech, Night Shade, Cruise, Spite, Will-O-Wisp, Faint Attack, Shadow Ball, Snatch, Grudge
Evolves: at level 37
Type: Ghost
Height: 2' 0"
Weight: 5 lbs

BANETTE

Marionette Pokémon
How to Say It: ban-NET
Possible Moves: Knock Off, Screech, Night Shade, Curse, Spite, Will-O-Wisp, Faint Attack, Shadow Ball, Snatch, Grudge
Does not evolve
Type: Ghost
Height: 3' 7"
Weight: 28 lbs

HOENN

Once **Duskull** gets going, it is tough to stop. It will follow an opponent wherever it goes. **Duskull** can even pass through walls!

Dusclops is the evolved form of **Duskull**. A weird Pokémon, **Dusclops** can absorb things into its body! It can also hypnotize you with its one big eye. So if you run into **Dusclops**, don't look at it! In fact, you might want to run away!

DUSKULL

Requiem Pokémon

How to Say It: DUHS-kuhl
Possible Moves: Leer, Night Shade, Disable, Foresight, Astonish, Confuse Ray, Pursuit, Curse, Will-O-Wisp, Mean Look, Future Sight
Evolves: at level 37
Type: Ghost
Height: 2' 7"
Weight: 33 lbs

DUSCLOPS

Beckon Pokémon

How to Say It: DUSS-klops
Possible Moves: Bind, Leer, Night Shade, Disable, Foresight, Astonish, Confuse Ray, Pursuit, Curse, Shadow Punch, Will-O-Wisp, Mean Look, Future Sight
Does not evolve
Type: Ghost
Height: 5' 3"
Weight: 67 lbs

• GHOSTLY TRAINERS •

As you travel around the Pokémon world, you will have to battle Gym Leaders to earn special badges. When you earn your badges, you can compete in the Pokémon League against the best Trainers around. Here are three who love Ghost-types the best. If you challenge them, you'll be in for a terrifying time!

TRAINER: Morty
LOCATION: Ectruteak Gym, Johto Region
KNOWN POKÉMON: A variety of Ghost-types, including Gastly, Haunter, Gengar, and Misdreavus. Morty also has Murkrow, a Dark-and-Flying type.
IF YOU WIN: If you defeat Morty, you will get a Fog Badge and a move called Shadow Ball.
THE DIRT ON MORTY: When Ash first met Morty's Ghost-types, they tricked him into thinking the Gym was on fire. Ash was not too happy, but when Team Rocket stole **Togepi**, the Ghost-type Pokémon saved the day! Ash went on to battle Morty and earn a Fog Badge.

TRAINER: Agatha
LOCATION: Indigo Plateau, Kanto Region
KNOWN POKÉMON: Gengar, Haunter, Golbat, Arbok, Muk, Venusaur
THE DIRT ON AGATHA: Agatha is one of the Elite Four. Most Trainers hate to face her because she uses many Ghost-and-Poison-type Pokémon, but you need to challenge Agatha if you want to compete in the Pokémon League. Your best bet against her? Try a Psychic-type, or a strong Ghost-type Pokémon.

TRAINER: Phoebe
LOCATION: Ever Grande City, Hoenn Region
KNOWN POKÉMON: Phoebe fights with two Dusclops, two Banette, and Sableye, a Dark-and-Ghost-type.
THE DIRT ON PHOEBE: Phoebe trained on Mt. Pyre, where she gained the ability to communicate with Ghost-types. Now she is a member of the Elite Four in the Hoenn Pokémon League. If you have a strong Dark-type on your team, you have a chance of defeating her.

• SPOOKY SPOTS •

You never know when you will encounter a Ghost-type Pokémon. They can appear out of nowhere! But if you are looking for Ghost-type Pokémon, there are a few places you can go to find them—if you dare!

Maiden's Peak

There is a legend about Maiden's Peak. A girl was in love with a sailor. She stood on the shore day after day waiting for him to come back. But he never did and she turned to stone. Now her ghost haunts Maiden's Peak once a year at the Summer's End festival. Brock and James from Team Rocket thought they saw the ghost of Maiden's Peak. What they really saw was **Gastly**, pretending to be the ghost! **Gastly** had to leave when the sun rose—but if you go to the next festival, you might see **Gastly** there again!

Hagatha's Forest

If you are traveling in the Johto region, you might come across a dark forest. An old woman named Hagatha will offer to rent you a **Hoothoot**. Do it!

The forest is filled with Ghost-type Pokémon. They love to cause illusions to scare travelers. But **Hoothoot** can see through the illusions. When you get through the forest, you just give **Hoothoot** to Hagatha's sister. Not a bad deal!

The Hoenn Port

When Ash decided to go to the Hoenn
region, he and **Pikachu** took a ship
there. Right as the ship landed, Team
Rocket stole **Pikachu**!

Pikachu and **Meowth** got
separated from Jessie and James.
They ended up in a bad part of town. A gang of
Haunter roamed the neighborhood. They
tried to scare **Pikachu** and **Meowth**—
but the two Pokémon chased them
off. Are you as brave as **Pikachu**
and **Meowth**? If you think so, catch
the next boat to the Hoenn region.
There is a gang of **Haunter** waiting
for you!

The Mansion of Shuppet

On the road to Fortree City, Ash and his
friends got stuck in a rainstorm. They found
shelter in an old mansion. It looked like it
was abandoned. But there were some scary
surprises there. . . .

First, Max went missing. Then Ash, May,
and Brock encountered Team Rocket, who
were busy trying to rob the mansion. Ash and the
others had to stop Team Rocket and find
Max. Luckily for Max, he met up with a friendly
Shuppet who lived in the mansion. Max
and **Shuppet** helped save the day!

BATTLE TIPS FOR DARK POKÉMON •

Once you catch a Dark-type Pokémon, you will need to learn how to battle with it. If you battle with a a Dark-type Pokémon, this chart will help you know which moves will do the most—or the least—damage to other Pokémon.

DARK-TYPES ARE GOOD AGAINST:

- Psychic-types such as Alakazam.
- Ghost-types such as Dusclops.

DARK-TYPES ARE BAD AGAINST:

- Fighting-types such as Makuhita.
- Steel-types such as Registeel.
- Other Dark-types.

Now you know how to battle with your Dark-type Pokémon. But that's not all you need to know to train these mysterious types. Keep reading to get the stats on every known Dark-type in the world of Pokémon!

Dark-type Pokémon are dangerous. Ghost-type Pokémon are scary. Now imagine a Pokémon that combines both types! That is spooky **Sableye**.

Many people are afraid of **Sableye**. They say that when its eyes glow, it will steal your spirit! Don't worry, though. You won't find a **Sableye** in your neighborhood. They live deep in caverns. They dig with their sharp claws, looking for rocks to eat. That's right—rocks! What a strange Pokémon!

SABLEYE

Darkness Pokémon

How to Say It: SAY-buhl-eye
Possible Moves: Leer, Scratch, Foresight, Night Shade, Astonish, Fury Swipes, Fake Out, Detect, Faint Attack, Knock Off, Confuse Ray, Shadow Ball, Mean Look
Does not evolve
Dual Type: Dark-Ghost
Height: 1' 8"
Weight: 24 lbs

Did You Know?

Sableye is the only Pokémon that is both Dark- and-Ghost-type. That's probably a good thing. When these two terrifying types mix, there's trouble brewing!

JOHTO

Most Pokémon Trainers are happy to find a Pokémon in the wild. But **Murkrow** is a different story. People believe that if you see **Murkrow** at night, you will have bad luck!

Believe it or not, **Murkrow** and **Meowth** have something in common. They both like to collect shiny objects. **Murkrow** steals shiny things that it finds. It might even steal a ring right off of your finger! **Murkrow** and **Meowth** steal from each other, too. Hmm. Which do you think would win in a battle?

MURKROW
Darkness Pokémon
How to Say It: MUR-kroe
Possible Moves: Peck, Astonish, Pursuit, Haze, Night Shade, Faint Attack, Taunt, Mean Look
Does not evolve
Dual Type: Dark-Flying
Height: 1' 8"
Weight: 5 lbs

Tip
Battling a **Hypno**? Then your **Murkrow** will come in handy. **Murkrow** has an Ability called Insomnia. That means that **Murkrow** can't be put asleep by **Hypno**'s Hypnosis Attack!

Houndour and **Houndoom** may look like dogs, but they are not like normal pets. **Houndour** like to run around the forest in packs. They work together to catch prey.

With its curved horns, **Houndoom** looks even scarier than **Houndour**. But not all **Houndoom** are scary. Once, Misty's **Togepi** got lost. A **Houndoom** found **Togepi** and it kept the little Pokémon safe until Misty found it again!

The best place to find these Dark-and-Fire-types is in the woods at night. Listen closely: If you hear strange, eerie howls, it might be **Houndour** and **Houndoom** calling to each other. Then it's up to you to see if you are brave enough to catch one!

HOUNDOUR

Dark-type Pokémon

How to Say It: hown-DOUR
Possible Moves: Leer, Ember, Roar, Smog, Bite, Faint Attack, Flamethrower, Crunch, Howl, Odor Sleuth
Evolves: at level 24
Dual Type: Dark-Fire
Height: 2' 0"
Weight: 24 lbs

HOUNDOOM

Dark-type Pokémon

How to Say It: hown-DOOM
Possible Moves: Faint Attack, Flamethrower, Leer, Odor Sleuth, Ember, Roar, Smog, Crunch, Howl, Bite
Does not evolve
Dual Type: Dark-Fire
Height: 4' 7"
Weight: 77 lbs

It is late at night. A full moon shines brightly in the sky. Suddenly, you see a weird glow nearby. What could it be?

It might be **Umbreon**. This Dark-type Pokémon is one of the five evolved forms of **Eevee**. **Umbreon** has special rings on its body. They glow at night, especially during a full moon. They also glow when **Umbreon** is about to attack. But you might not see **Umbreon** until it's too late. It will hide in the darkness, waiting for the right moment to leap out!

Eevee (Normal-type)

Tip

If you take good care of your **Eevee**, it can evolve through Friendship. If the Evolution happens during the day, it will evolve into **Espeon**. If it happens at night, **Eevee** will evolve into **Umbreon**!

UMBREON

Moonlight Pokémon

How to Say It: UHM-bree-on
Possible Moves: Tackle, Tail Whip, Helping Hand, Sand-Attack, Pursuit, Quick Attack, Confuse Ray, Faint Attack, Mean Look, Screech, Moonlight
Does not evolve
Type: Dark
Height: 3′ 3″
Weight: 60 lbs

Many Dark-type Pokémon can be sneaky or mean. **Sneasel** is a good example. This Pokémon uses its sharp claws to climb up trees. If it finds a **Pidgey** nest, it will chase the **Pidgey** away. Then it will steal the eggs left behind! Poor **Pidgey**.

Sneasel uses sharp claws in battle, too. Its claws are hidden in its paws. If **Sneasel** is attacked, the claws come out! Then Sneasel's opponent is in for a nasty surprise.

SNEASEL

Sharp Claw Pokémon

How to Say It: SNEE-zul

Possible Moves: Scratch, Leer, Taunt, Quick Attack, Screech, Faint Attack, Fury Swipes, Icy Wind, Slash, Beat Up, Metal Claw

Does not evolve

Dual Type: Dark-Ice

Height: 2' 11"

Weight: 62 lbs

Tip

Sneaky **Sneasel** can learn the move Thief. With Thief, **Sneasel** can steal an item from its opponent!

21

Boom . . . boom . . . boom. The earth quakes. The ground shakes. A mighty **Tyranitar** is stomping down from the mountains!

Tyranitar is one big, bad Pokémon. Its body is so strong that almost nothing can harm it. And, it is so powerful that it can destroy the mountains it lives in. All that strength makes **Tyranitar** something of a bully. It goes out looking for Pokémon to challenge, because it thinks it can't be beat! It takes a tough Trainer to capture a **Tyranitar**.

Larvitar
(Rock-
Ground type)

Pupitar
(Rock-
Ground type)

TYRANITAR

Armor Pokémon

How to Say It: tie-RAN-it-ar
Possible Moves: Leer, Sandstorm, Screech, Rock Slide, Thrash, Scary Face, Bite, Hyper Beam, Crunch, Earthquake
Does not evolve
Dual Type: Rock-Dark
Height: 6' 7"
Weight: 445 lbs

Did You Know?

Once Professor Elm gave Ash an egg that hatched into a **Larvitar**. Ash helped the shy Pokémon find its parents, but its mother, a **Tyranitar**, thought Ash had stolen its baby! Ash managed to reunite Larvitar with its mother without getting stomped on—and he stopped a gang of Pokémon poachers in the process!

It's not surprising that **Poochyena** has moves like Bite and Crunch, because this Bite Pokémon will eat almost anything! And this tough little Pokémon will bristle its tail to scare its opponents in battle.

When **Poochyena** evolves into **Mightyena**, it is just as tough on Trainers as it is on other Pokémon. If you catch a **Mightyena**, you had better be ready—these Pokémon remember running wild with their pack, and they only listen to the best Trainers.

POOCHYENA

Bite Pokémon

How to Say It: pooch-ee-YEH-nuh

Possible Moves: Tackle, Howl, Sand-Attack, Bite, Odor Sleuth, Roar, Swagger, Scary Face, Take Down, Taunt, Crunch, Thief

Evolves: at level 18

Type: Dark

Height: 1' 8"

Weight: 30 lbs

MIGHTYENA

Bite Pokémon

How to Say It: mite-ee-YEH-nuh

Possible Moves: Tackle, Howl, Sand-Attack, Bite, Odor Sleuth, Roar, Swagger, Scary Face, Take Down, Taunt, Crunch, Thief

Does not evolve

Type: Dark

Height: 3' 3"

Weight: 82 lbs

Nuzleaf and Shiftry are both Grass-and-Dark-type Pokémon. They evolve from a cute little Pokémon called Seedot.

But little Seedot gets scarier when it evolves. Nuzleaf lives deep in the forest and likes to jump out and scare people. It also makes a flute out of the leaf on top of it's head. Then it plays music that gives people the creeps!

Shiftry is even more mysterious. It holds fans made out of leaves in its hands. When it waves the fans, it makes wind storms. If you get too close to Shiftry, you might get blown away!

NUZLEAF

Wily Pokémon

How to Say It: NUZZ-leef

Possible Moves: Pound, Harden, Growth, Nature Power, Fake Out, Torment, Faint Attack, Razor Wind, Swagger, Extrasensory

Evolves: with a Leaf Stone

Dual Type: Grass-Dark

Height: 3' 3"

Weight: 62 lbs

SHIFTRY

Wicked Pokémon

How to Say It: SHIF-tree

Possible Moves: Pound, Harden, Growth, Nature Power

Does not evolve

Dual Type: Grass-Dark

Height: 4' 3"

Weight: 131 lbs

Seedot (Grass-type)

You're at sea, sailing in a boat. Suddenly, you hear a sickening sound. Something has ripped the bottom of the boat! It might be **Carvanha** or its evolved form, **Sharpedo**. Both Pokémon can rip up boats with their sharp teeth.

Carvanha will attack anything that invades its territory. And **Sharpedo** is feared throughout the ocean. It is nicknamed "The Bully of the Sea." If one of **Sharpedo**'s fangs falls out, a new one will grow right back in its place! So be on the lookout for these two next time you're in the ocean.

SHARPEDO

Brutal Pokémon

How to Say It: shar-PEE-doe
Possible Moves: Leer, Bite, Rage, Focus Energy, Scary Face, Crunch, Screech, Slash, Taunt, Swagger, Skull Bash, Agility
Does not evolve
Dual Type: Water-Dark
Height: 5' 11"
Weight: 196 lbs

CARVANHA

Savage Pokémon

How to Say It: car-VAHN-uh
Possible Moves: Leer, Bite, Rage, Focus Energy, Scary Face, Crunch, Screech, Take Down, Swagger, Agility
Evolves: at level 30
Dual Type: Water-Dark
Height: 2' 7"
Weight: 46 lbs

HOENN

During the day, this Pokémon might look like any other scarecrow watching over a field. It stays still so it doesn't dry out in the hot sun. But at night, this creepy Pokémon comes to life!

Cacturne like to hang together in groups. They wait until they see a traveler walking through the desert. The **Cacturne** will follow and wait until the traveler grows tired. And then . . . they go in for the attack! **Cacturne** is super creepy!

CACTURNE

Scarecrow Pokémon

How to Say It: CACK-turn
Possible Moves: Revenge, Poison Sting, Leer, Absorb, Growth, Leech Seed, Sand-Attack, Pin Missile, Ingrain, Faint Attack, Spikes, Needle Arm, Cotton Spore, Sandstorm, Destiny Bond
Does not evolve
Dual Type: Grass-Dark
Height: 4' 3"
Weight: 171 lbs

Tip

Trapinch, a Ground Pokémon, can blast its opponents with an attack called Sandstorm. If you face a **Trapinch** in battle, bring out your **Cacturne**! This Grass-and-Dark-type Pokémon has the ability Sand Veil, which lets **Cacturne** evade the Sandstorm attack.

Cacnea (Grass-type)

It takes a pretty brave Trainer to catch a **Crawdaunt**! This Water-and-Dark-type Pokémon will attack anything that comes near it. For that reason, most Pokémon will not live near **Crawdaunt**, which live by themselves in dark, lonely ponds.

There is one time when **Crawdaunt** won't attack: When it sheds its shell, it buries itself in the mud. It won't come out until a new, hard shell grows. But when it comes back out—watch out!

Did You Know?

Ash doesn't have any Dark-type Pokémon. But he does have the Water Pokémon **Corphish** on his team. Will **Corphish** ever evolve into the Water-and-Dark-type Pokémon **Crawdaunt**? Only time will tell!

CRAWDAUNT

Rogue Pokémon

How to Say It: CRAW-daunt
Possible Moves: Bubble, Harden, Vicegrip, Leer, Bubblebeam, Knock Off, Taunt, Protect, Crabhammer, Swords Dance, Crunch, Guillotine
Does not evolve
Dual Type: Water-Dark
Height: 3' 7"
Weight: 72 lbs

Corphish
(Water-type)

HOENN

This Dark-type Pokémon does something no other Pokémon can do: **Absol** can predict when a disaster will happen! People say if you see an **Absol**, something dangerous might be coming—like an earthquake, tidal wave, or storm. That's why **Absol** is known as a Disaster Pokémon.

If you want to catch an **Absol**, you will probably have to go climbing. **Absol** live in the mountains, and they almost never come down. Unless, of course, a disaster is on the way!

ABSOL

Disaster Pokémon

How to Say It: AB-sole

Possible Moves: Scratch, Leer, Taunt, Quick Attack, Razor Wind, Bite, Swords Dance, Double Team, Slash, Future Sight, Perish Song

Does not evolve

Type: Dark

Height: 3' 11"

Weight: 104 lbs

Tip

Some people wear sunglasses when it's sunny. So what kind of glasses do you give your Dark-type Pokémon? Blackglasses, of course! When held by a Pokémon, they increase the power of its attacks.

• A DARK TALE •

You might already know that Ash battled a Trainer named Harrison in the Silver League. Before they met on the battlefield, Ash and Harrison had an adventure with a wild **Sneasel**. Here's what happened. . . .

Ages ago, Mishiro Town in the Johto Region was the site of many wars and battles. **Ho-Oh** purified the land with its fire. Soon, the plants and trees grew back, and Pokémon roamed free again.

The last bit of **Ho-Oh**'s fire was saved in a temple. The people of Mishiro Town guarded the Sacred Fire for years.

But when Ash and his friends arrived in Mishiro Town, they learned that **Sneasel** was keeping people away from the temple, with help from a wild **Machop** and **Machoke**. Ash volunteered to help catch the **Sneasel** and free the sacred fire.

A Trainer named Harrison asked to go along with Ash. He wanted to catch the **Sneasel** for himself. When they got to the temple, **Machop** and **Machoke** attacked with their Fighting-type moves. Misty sent out her **Corsola**. Harrison sent out his **Houndoom**. The two Pokémon quickly knocked down **Machop** and **Machoke**.

Ash spotted the **Sneasel**. He sent **Totodile** to battle it. **Totodile** slammed **Sneasel** with Water Gun. But **Sneasel** quickly replied with Slash. Then **Sneasel** used Shadow Ball. **Totodile** slammed into Ash, and the two went flying back!

When Ash recovered, Team Rocket was trying to steal **Sneasel**. The sneaky Dark Pokémon tricked Team Rocket. But **Machop** and **Machoke** were back in the fight.

Ash called on **Phanpy**. *Slam!* **Phanpy** tackled **Machop**. Harrison called on **Houndoom**. *Wham!* **Houndoom** used Take Down on **Machoke**.

Then **Houndoom** called on his **Blaziken**. Ash had never seen the Fire-and-Fighting-type Pokémon before. The powerful Pokémon blasted **Sneasel** with Flamethrower and Fire Punch.

Zap! Harrison quickly caught **Sneasel** in his Poké Ball.

Ash felt great. He had helped to save the Sacred Fire. Little did he know that Harrison would use **Sneasel** against him in battle before long. . . .

• THEY LIKE THE DARK SIDE •

It takes a special kind of Trainer to work with Dark-type Pokémon. Dark-type Pokémon can sometimes be sneaky, tricky, angry, or hard to predict. Meet three Trainers who think Dark-types are the best types around.

TRAINER: Sidney
LOCATION: Ever Grande City, Hoenn Region
KNOWN POKÉMON: Mightyena, Shiftry, Cacturne, Sharpedo, Absol

THE DIRT ON SIDNEY: If you want to compete in the Hoenn Pokémon League, you will need to beat the Trainers known as the Elite Four. Sidney is the first you'll face. His team is full of Dark-types. If you have Fighting or Bug-types on your team, you'll stand a chance of beating Sidney.

TRAINER: Harrison
LOCATION: Hoenn Region
KNOWN POKÉMON: Kecleon, Sneasel, Hypno, Steelix, Houndoom, Blaziken

THE DIRT ON HARRISON: Harrison does not specialize in Dark-types, but he has two tough ones on his team: **Sneasel** and **Houndoom**. Harrison battled Ash in the Silver League conference in the Johto Region. Harrison almost won the battle with his **Houndoom**. In the end, Harrison's **Blaziken** battled Ash's **Charizard**, and won.

TRAINER: Gary Oak
LOCATION: originally from the Johto Region
KNOWN POKÉMON: Gary has more than 200 Pokémon, including Nidoking, Nidoqueen, Arcanine, Doduo, and his favorite—Umbreon.
THE DIRT ON GARY: Gary is Professor Oak's grandson. Gary and Ash started their Pokémon journeys at the same time and have been rivals ever since. Gary has had his **Umbreon** since it started out as an **Eevee**. Ash might not always like Gary's attitude but he has to admit that Gary is a good Trainer. You have to treat an **Eevee** really well to get it to evolve into an **Umbreon**!

BATTLE TIPS FOR STEEL-TYPES

Every Pokémon Trainer should have a Steel Pokémon on their team. What should you do with it once you get it? If you battle with a Steel Pokémon, this chart will help you to know which moves will do the most—or the least—damage to other Pokémon.

STEEL-TYPES ARE GOOD AGAINST:

- Ice-types such as Regice.
- Rock-types such as Sudowoodo.

STEEL-TYPES ARE BAD AGAINST:

- Electric-types such as Pikachu.
- Fire-types such as Torchic.
- Water-types such as Totodile.
- Other Steel-types.

Now you know how to battle with your Steel-type Pokémon. But that's not all you need to know to train these supertough types. Read on to get the stats on every known Steel-type in the world of Pokémon!

Sometimes you *can* judge a book by its cover. If you look at a **Scizor** and think it's one tough Pokémon, you're right! Scizor is the final evolution of **Scyther**. After it evolves, **Scizor**'s body becomes as hard as steel. Its large pincers are made of steel, too. They can crush hard objects.

Scizor's razor-sharp pincers have another special feature. They have patterns on them that look like eyes. When **Scizor** waves its pincers around, its opponent thinks that Scizor has three heads! But this superstrong Pokémon only needs one head to win.

SCIZOR

Scissors Pokémon

How to Say It: SIE-zor

Possible Moves: Quick Attack, Leer, Focus Energy, Pursuit, False Swipe, Agility, Metal Claw, Slash, Swords Dance, Iron Defense, Fury Cutter

Does not evolve

Dual Type: Bug-Steel

Height: 5' 11"

Weight: 260 lbs

Tip

A must-have for all Steel Pokémon Trainers is Metal Coat! This handy item will increase your Steel Pokémon's attack power. You can also use it to help evolve **Scyther** into **Scizor**, and **Onix** into **Steelix**.

Scyther
(Bug-Flying type)

JOHTO

What does this Pokémon have in common with a diamond? **Steelix** is made out of the same material as a diamond, but **Steelix** is even harder!

Don't feel like battling? Then put your **Steelix** out in the sun and watch the small metal particles that cover its body reflect the sun. **Steelix** evens sparkles like a diamond!

Onix
(Rock-Ground type)

STEELIX

Iron Serpent Pokémon

How to Say It: STEEL-icks

Possible Moves: Tackle, Screech, Bind, Rock Throw, Harden, Rage, Dragonbreath, Sandstorm, Slam, Iron Tail, Crunch, Double-Edge

Does not evolve

Dual Type: Steel-Ground

Height: 30' 02"

Weight: 882 lbs

Tip

If you have a **Steelix**, then teach it a move called Iron Tail. You can use it to lower your opponent's defense so **Steelix** can finish it off!

Imagine a bird that is made out of steel, but can still fly high. You've just pictured **Skarmory**, a tough Steel-and-Flying-type Pokémon. Even **Skarmory**'s feathers are dangerous. Its wings have supersharp cutting edges. People once used the feathers as swords!

Think being made out of steel slows this bird down? Its wings may look heavy, but they're actually hollow and light. They allow **Skarmory** to combine speed with the power of steel.

SKARMORY

Armor Bird Pokémon

How to Say It: SCAR-muh-ree

Possible Moves: Leer, Peck, Sand-Attack, Swift, Agility, Fury Attack, Air Cutter, Steel Wing, Spikes, Metal Sound

Does not evolve

Dual Type: Steel-Flying

Height: 5' 07"

Weight: 111 lbs

Did You Know?

Are you facing an opponent who uses **Marowak**? This Ground-type Pokémon can pound your Pokémon senseless with its Thick Club move. But if you have a **Skarmory**, you're in luck! **Skarmory** is one of the few Pokémon that can survive **Marowak**'s attack.

STEEL • STEEL • STEEL • STEEL •

KANTO, JOHTO, & HOENN

Lights out! **Magnemite** feeds on electricity. Sometimes a bunch of **Magnemite** will drain all of the electricity out of a house. Then the power goes out!

Magnemite combines electric power with magnetic power. It uses that power to float through the air. **Magnemite**'s power can make it stick to other **Magnemite**. When three **Magnemite** stick together, they form a Magneton.

Magneton like to mess with the power and radio waves in cities. They also appear when there are spots on the sun. But don't get too close—**Magneton** give off strange waves of energy. They can give you an earache!

MAGNETON
Magnet Pokémon
How to Say It: MAG-nuh-tun
Possible Moves: Tackle, Sonicboom, Thundershock, Supersonic, Thunder Wave, Screech, Metal Sound, Spark, Lock-On, Tri Attack, Zap Cannon
Does not evolve
Dual Type: Electric-Steel
Height: 3' 3"
Weight: 132 lbs

MAGNEMITE
Magnet Pokémon
How to Say It: MAG-nuh-mite
Possible Moves: Sonicboom, Thundershock, Supersonic, Thunder Wave, Swift, Screech, Metal Sound, Tackle, Spark, Lock-On, Zap Cannon
Evolves: at level 30
Dual Type: Electric-Steel
Height: 1' 0"
Weight: 13 lbs

36

Looking for a **Forretress**? Then go for a walk in the woods. Check the biggest, fattest tree trunks. **Forretress**, like its pre-evolved form, **Pineco**, likes to hang on to a tree. But look out! **Forretress** will shoot out bits of its hard shell if it thinks you are a threat. And because **Forretress'** shell is made out of steel, this can hurt!

Nobody knows what is inside **Forretress'** tough shell. It is only opened when this Steel-type Pokémon catches its prey. But it does it so fast you can't peek inside!

Pineco
(Bug-type)

FORRETRESS

Bagworm Pokémon

How to Say It: FOUR-eh-tress
Possible Moves: Tackle, Protect, Selfdestruct, Take Down, Rapid Spin, Bide, Zap Cannon, Explosion, Spikes, Double-Edge
Does not evolve
Dual Type: Bug-Steel
Height: 3' 11"
Weight: 277 lbs

Did You Know?

One of Brock's favorite Pokémon is his **Forretress**! He owned the Pokémon when it was still just a **Pineco**. But **Pineco** evolved into **Forretress** to help Brock send Team Rocket blasting off!

HOENN

These unusual Steel-and-Psychic-type Pokémon start out as **Beldum**. **Beldum** can communicate with other **Beldum** by sending out magnetic pulses. When two **Beldum** fuse together, they evolve into one **Metang**. The **Beldum**'s brains join together, giving **Metang** super strong psychokinetic powers. When two **Metang** fuse together, they evolve into **Metagross**, giving it a total of four brains!

BELDUM

Iron Ball Pokémon

How to Say It: BELL-dum
Possible Moves: Take Down
Evolves: at level 20
Dual Type: Steel-Psychic
Height: 2' 0"
Weight: 210 lbs

Did You Know?

Beldum, **Metagross**, and **Metang** all have the special Ability Clear Body. This protects the Pokémon from attacks that lower their stats. For example, if a **Mightyena** attacks **Beldum** with Scary Face, **Beldum**'s stats will not change.

METANG

Iron Claw Pokémon

How to Say It: meh-TANG

Possible Moves: Take Down, Confusion, Metal Claw, Scary Face, Pursuit, Psychic, Iron Defense, Meteor Mash, Agility, Hyper Beam

Evolves: at level 45

Dual Type: Steel-Psychic

Height: 3' 11"

Weight: 447 lbs

METAGROSS

Iron Leg Pokémon

How to Say It: MEH-uh-gross

Possible Moves: Take Down, Confusion, Metal Claw, Scary Face, Confusion, Pursuit, Psychic, Iron Defense, Meteor Mash, Agility, Hyper Beam

Does not evolve

Dual Type: Steel-Psychic

Height: 5' 3"

Weight: 1,213 lbs

HOENN

Do you think **Aron** orders a pizza when it's hungry? Nope. This Pokémon likes to munch on iron ore. It will eat rocks, bridges—even trucks! When **Aron** evolves into **Lairon**, it adds mineral spring water to its diet. The evolved form of **Lairon**, **Aggron** likes to live on a mountain. This Pokémon will battle anybody who tries to come onto its mountain home.

Tip

Aron and **Lairon** are both Steel-and-Rock-types. If you catch a wild **Aron** or **Lairon**, it might have the Item Hard Stone. This item increases the power of the Rock-type Pokémon that holds it.

ARON

Iron Armor Pokémon

How to Say It: AH-ron

Possible Moves: Tackle, Harden, Mud-Slap, Headbutt, Metal Claw, Iron Defense, Roar, Take Down, Iron Tail, Protect, Metal Sound, Double-Edge

Evolves: at level 32

Dual Type: Steel-Rock

Height: 1' 4"

Weight: 132 lbs